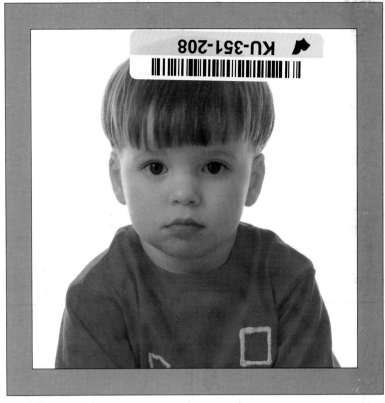

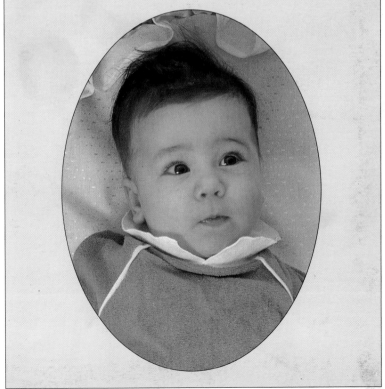

For Mike – D.M.
For Alan, Harriet and Tom – A.S.

First published in Great Britain in 1992 by
Frances Lincoln Limited, 4 Torriano Mews
Torriano Avenue, London NW5 2RZ

British Library Cataloguing in Publication Data
available on request

ISBN 0-7112-0702-X

Set in Univers Light by FMT Graphics
Printed in Hong Kong

Design and Art Direction Debbie MacKinnon

3 5 7 9 8 6 4 2

WHAT SHAPE? ☆

Debbie MacKinnon
Photographs by Anthea Sieveking

FRANCES LINCOLN

What shape is Claudia's tunnel?

It's round.

more round things

teething ring

bowl

tomato

clock

balls

What shape is Oliver's sandpit?

It's square.

more squares

activity toy

dice

book

jigsaw puzzle

soft blocks

What shape is Gemma's tent?

It's a triangle.

more triangles

cheese

sandwiches

paper napkin

cake

party hat

pizza

What shape is Grace's present?

It's a rectangle.

more rectangles

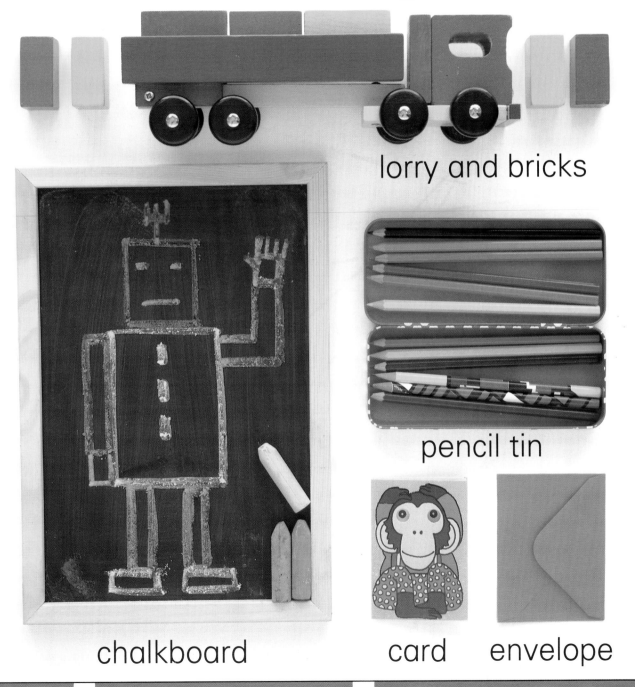

lorry and bricks

chalkboard

pencil tin

card   envelope

What shape
is Jack's
basket?

It's an
oval.

more ovals

chocolate eggs

baby's shoes

grapes

pebbles

pine cone

egg

sponge

What shape is
Andy's balloon?

It's a
heart.

more hearts

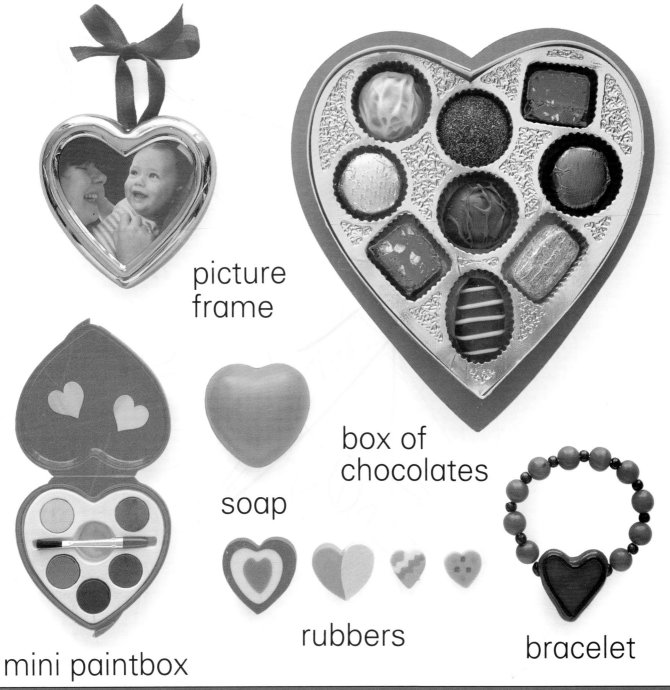

picture frame

box of chocolates

soap

mini paintbox

rubbers

bracelet

What shape is Sabrina's wand?

It's a star.

more stars

biscuits

stickers

biscuit cutters

starfish

baby's toy

sunglasses

What
shape
are Sam's
buttons?

They
are
diamonds

more diamonds

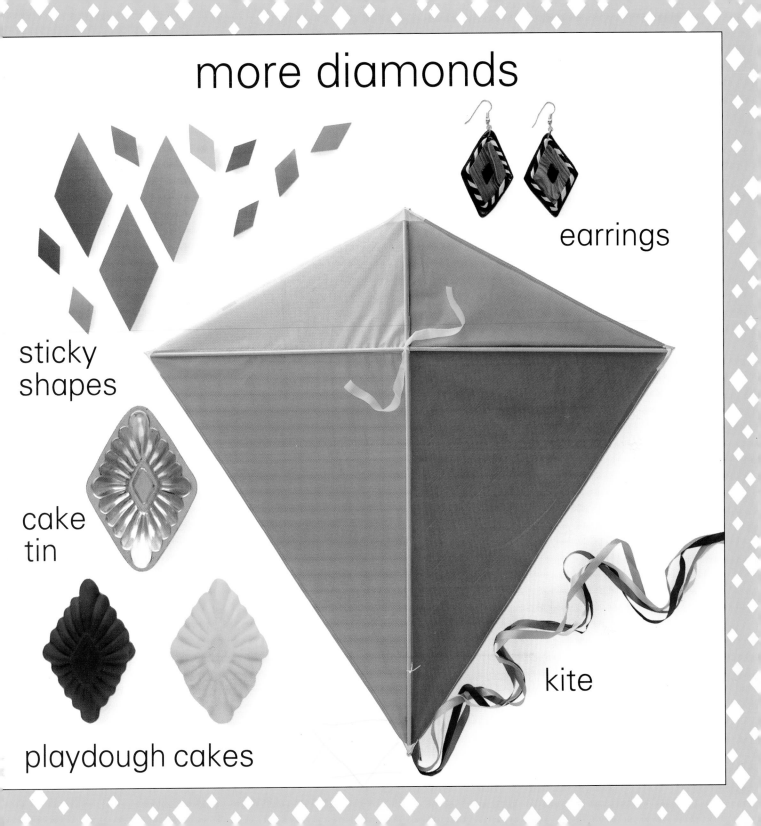

earrings

sticky
shapes

cake
tin

playdough cakes

kite

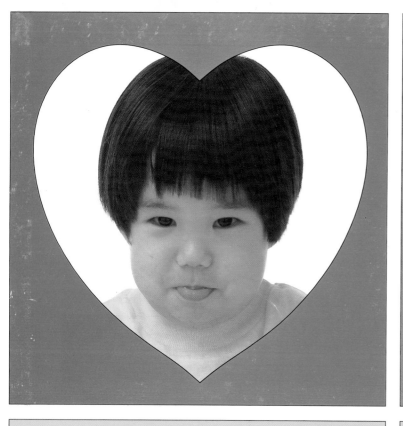